Raise the Bar
Grades 3-5

Piano

Teaching Notes written by Graham Fitch

Published by
Trinity College London Press
www.trinitycollege.com

Registered in England
Company no. 09726123

Copyright © 2016 Trinity College London Press
First impression, April 2016

Printed in England by Caligraving Ltd.

Contents

Teaching Notes – Grade 3

Romance (Marais)

This attractive flowing piece features a singing RH over a light walking bass. Sing the RH line to discover how to shape it, and where it needs to breathe. The RH may assist by taking some bass notes if this helps the LH to avoid some of the bigger stretches.

Experiment with different touches in the LH; you may play the bass line lightly detached, or using a combination of *legato* and *staccato*. As a general rule, stepwise passages (bars 8, 9, 11, 12 etc) sound best when played more *legato*, and passages with larger intervals (such as the opening) more detached. Play the ornaments with melodic shape, always starting on the beat. In the Baroque period composers gave very few performance markings, if any. The important thing is always to play musically, and never mechanically. If you play the repeats, you may vary the dynamics.

Allegro in E minor (Agrell)

This **Allegro** movement has an expressive focus; we feel pathos and perhaps even lamenting. There are two main ideas. The first idea (bars 1-8) features descending chromatic lines (syncopated between the hands), and sighing figures. The second idea (bars 9-20) is more open, with rising broken chord patterns and larger intervals. The main cadence points clearly establish the relative major, G (at the double bar), and the home key (at the end).

The metronome marking reflects the expressive details of the music. Stress the first (dissonant) note of each of the appoggiaturas (bars 10, 12, etc) and play the resolution very softly. The texture of the LH in bars 21-26 and 57-63 thickens and becomes richer with the introduction of a tenor line. Hold the tied crotchets over the bar line and play this line very expressively (these phrases echo the sighs in the top voice).

Allegro (Pergolesi)

This two-part **Allegro** is a duo between the hands, both of which are equally important. The unmarked quavers are best played detached, but some short slurs are possible depending on your taste. Some dynamic suggestions have been added, but Pergolesi left none. You might make use of sudden dynamic changes from f to p, as well as graded *crescendos* and *diminuendos*. For example, descending sequential patterns (bars 5-8) lend themselves to a *diminuendo*; ascending ones (bars 38-40) to a *crescendo*. Ornaments in this period are played on the beat (the ornament starts together with the LH). The appoggiaturas (bars 8, 25, 27 etc) are melodic and expressive in effect; the acciaccaturas (bars 11 and 20) add sharp rhythmic accents to the line.

Bourrée in A minor (Krebs)

A bourrée is a courtly dance of French origin, characterised by phrases that begin with an upbeat. This example by Krebs needs a carefully managed tempo. To give the feeling of a relaxed four in a bar, make sure the third beat is weaker than the first (and the second and fourth beats weaker still).

To bring the qualities of poise and elegance to this dance, lightly detach the LH crotchets; they should certainly not be too short, though. Quaver patterns in both hands need melodic shaping. Allow the music to breathe by making a small separation between each phrase in the RH – this involves shortening the last note of each phrase somewhat. When you play the repeats, you may vary the dynamics and even add suitable ornaments.

Allegretto (Gurlitt)

This Allegretto in G is in ternary (ABA) form. The first idea (bars 1-2) needs very expressive handling whenever it recurs. To bring out the sighing quality, give a little weight to the first notes in both hands. Taper the sound carefully as you cross the bar line, so that the short phrase ends very gently and without an accent. Play the answering phrase (bars 3-4) gracefully, with the LH very light (attending to precise note lengths).

The more assertive B section (bars 17-24) is in the dominant key of D major, the mood darkening as it moves to D minor (bar 25). The flowing RH semiquaver patterns here need to be very even in time and tone. The long, held RH F (from bar 30) heralds the return to C major, after which the A section is repeated exactly.

Melody (Khachaturian)

Melody features a singing RH line over a chordal LH, and is gently expressive and somewhat melancholy in character. Notice the way Khachaturian uses the chromatic scale in the left hand accompaniment.

Legato pedal is needed throughout the piece to sustain the repeated LH chords and to add colour and resonance to the sound. Bars 1-2 can be played in one pedal. As a general rule think about changing the pedal when the harmony changes. Listen to make sure that the chord changes are always clear. At the return of the opening melody in bar 18 the LH takes on a lilting accompaniment, but do ensure that the LH thumb is not emphasised.

Spanish Dance (Kelly)

It is very easy to feel the spinning movement in the quaver patterns of this colourful and descriptive piece. Your task as performer is to bring out the humour in the music. Bar 5 is an extra bar tacked onto the first phrase, and the effect is as though the dancers have lost their footing. The rests in the phrase beginning in bar 10 certainly give a feeling of hesitation, and the way the final cadence is interrupted (from bar 42) suggests giddiness from too much spinning.

Rhythmic precision and accuracy are required here, and the accents need to be very clear and incisive. Hold the pedal through the last 2 bars, and enjoy the final flourish. The last chord is not A minor as we might expect, but something much more exotic.

Jig (Hurd)

This modern Jig is a lively dance in compound quadruple time. The piece is built from major triads that step up and down in whole tones, G being the tonal centre. This gives the piece a strong modal flavour, thus a conventional key signature is not necessary. The piece is short enough to warrant the repeats; the first ending has an amusing interrupted cadence and it would be a shame to miss it.

Follow the phrase markings carefully; these are like musical punctuation marks (such as commas and full stops) and they allow the music to breathe. The technical challenges are in the RH as it sprints through broken chord and scale patterns. Try both the given fingerings to see which is the better one for your hand (every hand is different and unique).

Romance

Marin Marais
(1656-1728)

Dynamic markings are editorial.

Allegro in E minor

Johan Joachim Agrell
(1701-1765)

Dynamic markings and phrasing are editorial.

Allegro

from A Second Set of Lessons [Sonatas], no. 7 in E major

Giovanni Battista Pergolesi
(1710-1736)

Dynamic markings and phrasing are editorial.

Bourrée in A Minor

Johann Ludwig Krebs
(1713-1780)

Dynamic markings and articulation are editorial.

Allegretto

from *Sonatina in G*

Cornelius Gurlitt
(1820-1901)

Melody

('Ivan Sings')

Aram Khatchaturian
(1903-1978)

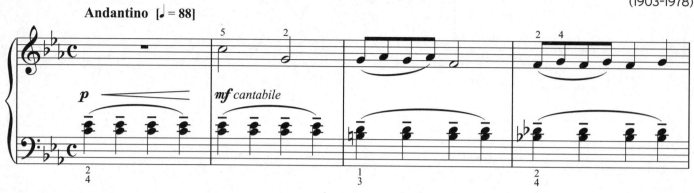

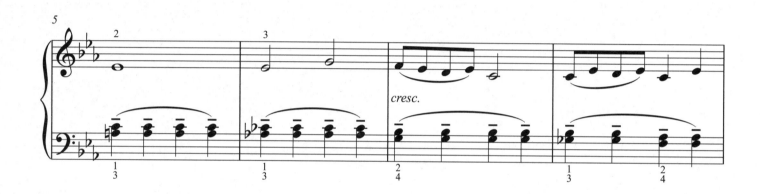

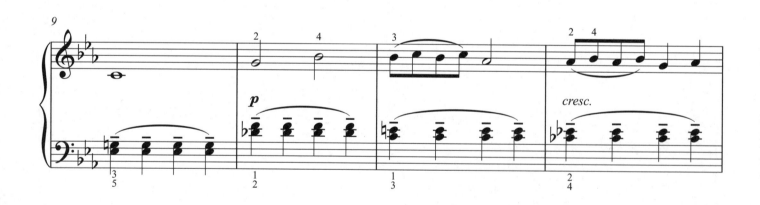

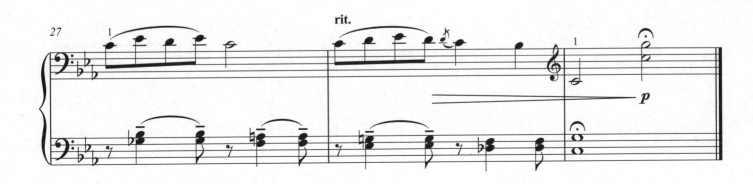

Spanish Dance

Bryan Kelly
(b. 1934)

Jig

Michael Hurd
(1928-2006)

Teaching Notes – Grade 4

Pavan: The Earle of Salisbury (Byrd)

Renaissance composer William Byrd wrote this Pavan for the harpsichord or virginals, in memory of Robert Cecil, the 1st Earl of Salisbury. The music is built from two eight-bar phrases, both of which are repeated; try dynamic contrasts to bring a change of colour to the repeats and to make the overall shape clear.

In early music performers used a more articulated touch in general, and some gentle breaks in the line are stylistically quite correct. Quavers that appear after dotted crotchets, for example, may be lightly detached.

Allegro in A major (W F Bach)

Wilhelm Friedemann was the eldest son of J S Bach, and a noted composer in his own right. This charming **Allegro** is in ternary form (ABA), with a graceful A section featuring a balanced phrase structure and tonic and dominant harmonies. The B section, in A minor, is more serious and darker in mood, with chromatic passing notes. In bar 23, notice how the B♭ darkens the perfect cadence to the tonic minor (the harmony on the first beat, built on the flattened second degree of the scale in first inversion, is known as a Neapolitan sixth).

Neatness and clarity of touch are called for throughout, with precision of attack and release in RH double thirds (bars 3-4, 9-10 etc, and the rising sequence from bar 28), and carefully articulated short slurs. Make sure to observe all dynamics and marks of expression as these help to bring the music to life.

Andante con espressione (Clementi)

This expressive movement is a study in tonal control and balance. The RH double notes need to be voiced to the upper note so that the main melodic line can be clearly heard.

Notice how Clementi embellishes the lines and varies the texture of the opening phrase each time it returns; there is always a new surprise for us. Pedal may be used in bars 1-4 and elsewhere, but beware of covering slurs and *staccatos*. Aim for delicacy as the music explores the upper registers of the piano (ie in the *dolce* of bars 21-22), and enjoy opening up the sound in the $f\!f$ at the end.

Scherzo (Hummel)

The term scherzo means 'joke', and while this example by Hummel is certainly light in spirit, there is some darkness in the middle section (from bar 17). There is one overall tempo throughout, although a slight easing is possible in bar 44 as we prepare the return to the opening section. Unmarked quavers need a light *staccato* touch. It is well worth practising the LH alone from bar 61-72, aiming for a *legato* in the tenor line according to the phrase lengths.

As with all fast pieces, it is a great idea to practise this slowly to start with, until you have developed the necessary precision in touch and control of the nimble fingerwork.

Study in E minor (Bertini)

This is a study in rhythmic evenness and finger control of fast triplet patterns, which both hands are required to execute with equal skill. The tempo is lively and the mood turbulent.

Make sure both hands sound precisely together at the beginning and end of the slurred triplet groups (ie bars 1-2), and taper the phrase off so we hear a very clear *diminuendo*. Crotchets not under a phrase mark should be detached (assume a *staccato* touch). The slurs in bars 8 and 16 apply to the triplets only; the crotchet above will be short. Pay careful attention to the part writing in the RH in bars 11-12; insist that long notes are held and shorter notes released. Avoid a *crescendo* through bar 14 – the $f\!f$ at bar 15 needs to be sudden and dramatic.

Suite de Danzas Criollas (1) (Ginastera)

This atmospheric movement in barcarolle style from Alberto Ginastera's *Creole Dance Suite* features piquant harmonies made up of chords with added notes and tone clusters. **Adagietto** is more light-hearted than **adagio**, so let the music move along while still giving breathing space at the ends of the phrases.

Texture is all-important in this piece. Layer the sound so that the melody line is in the foreground, allowing the harmonies to waft like smoke in the background. In bar 5 (and similar places) the top RH D should ring out gently like a bell, the chord that follows light as a feather. Generous pedalling is essential to allow the harmonies to build up throughout the bar, so pedal in whole bars (ie bars 1-8) according to the phrase markings.

Kleine Elegie (Schmitz)

The melody line formed by the long notes in the RH (stems up) is a very simple diatonic tune in C major with regular phrase lengths. It is worth playing the melody through once or twice by itself, perhaps singing along.

In Schmitz's setting of this tune each melody note comes at the start of unequal groups of quavers, often going against the beat (don't be put off by this unconventional notation). This gives the feeling of rhythmic flexibility and freedom even though the pulse is strict. It's an interesting effect! Hold LH notes through several changes of pedal where marked, and observe the composer's instruction to play the repeat.

Hänschen Klein (Lachenmann)

Hänschen Klein ('Little Hans') is an unconventional setting of a traditional German children's song in which the rhythm of the song is used but not the pitches. Instead, the piece is built from a descending chromatic scale (firstly in single notes and later in chromatic major thirds) starting at the very top of the piano and gradually working its way down to the bottom. There are all sorts of eerie sound effects to be explored in this piece.

Lachenmann writes for the piano in a contemporary way. The diamond note heads (bar 5, 19, etc) indicate that keys should be put down silently, thereby raising these dampers and allowing the strings to vibrate when other notes are played. From bar 9, the lines after the note heads indicate how long the finger should remain on the key. Follow pedal markings scrupulously, and enjoy the magical sound effects (especially in $f\!f\!f$).

Pavan: The Earle of Salisbury

William Byrd
(1543-1623)

[Maestoso ma espressivo ♩ = 72]

Allegro in A Major

Wilhelm Friedemann Bach
(1710-1784)

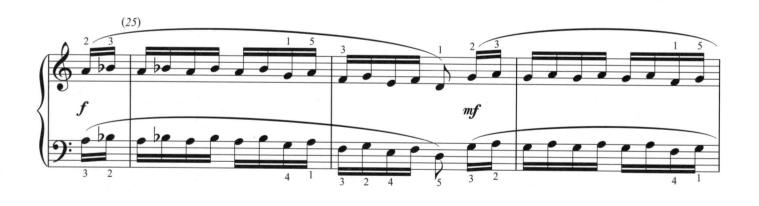

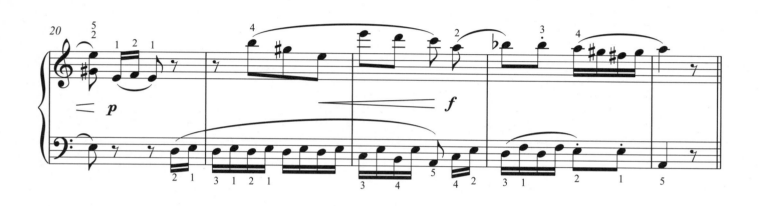

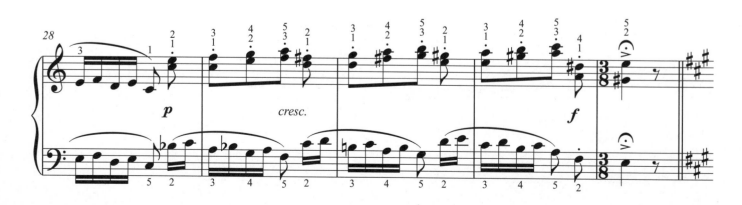

Andante con espressione

from *Sonatina in F*, op. 36 no. 4

Muzio Clementi
(1752–1832)

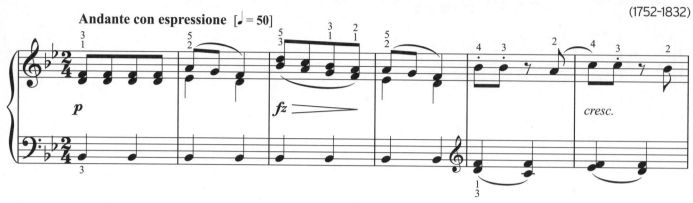

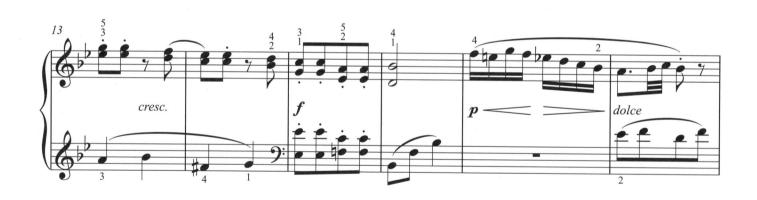

Scherzo

Johann Nepomuk Hummel
(1778-1837)

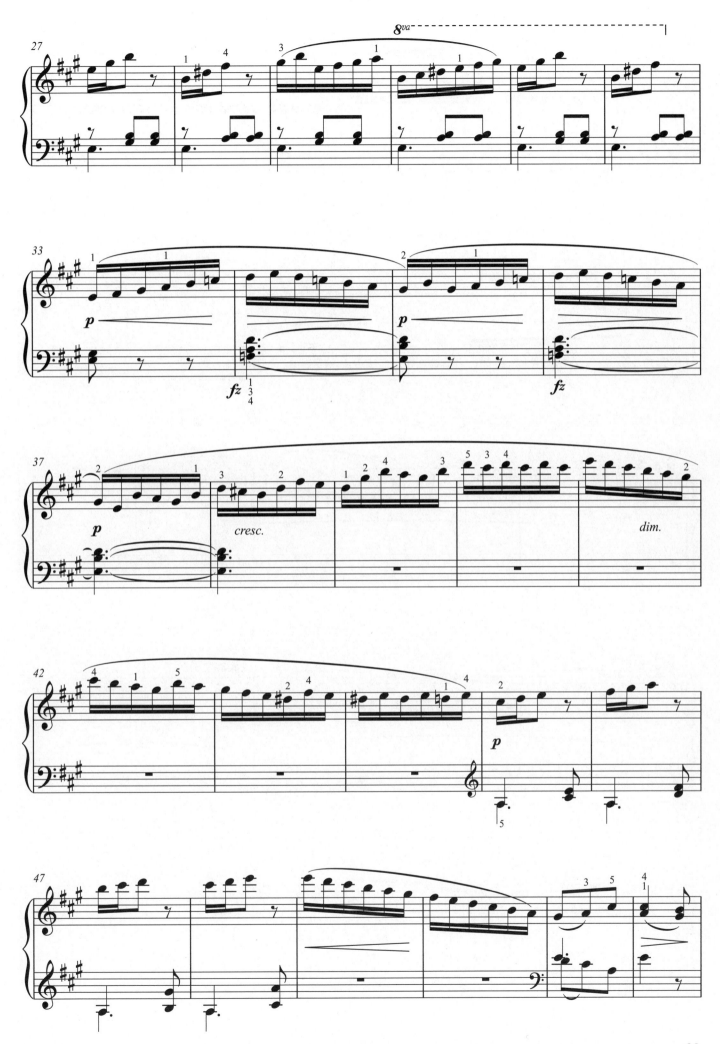

30

Study in E Minor

op. 29 no. 14

Henri Bertini
(1798–1876)

Suite de Danzas Criollas (1)

Alberto Ginastera
(1916-1983)

Kleine Elegie

Little Elegy from 'Rainbow Preludes'

Manfred Schmitz
(1939–2014)

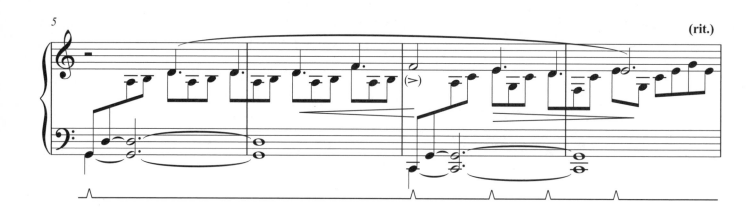

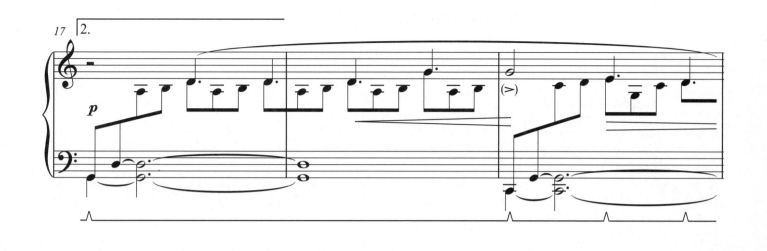

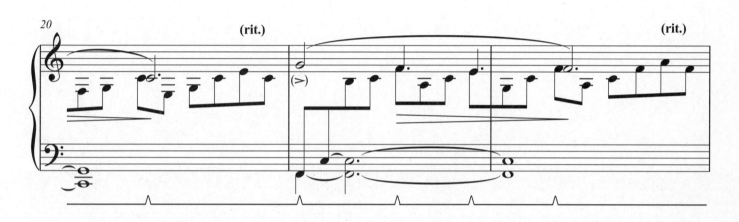

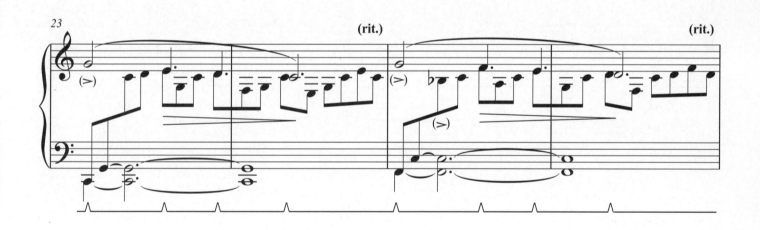

Hänschen Klein

from *Ein Kinderspiel*, 1980

Helmut Lachenmann
(b. 1935)

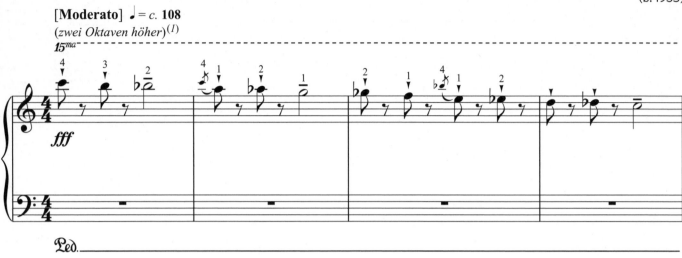

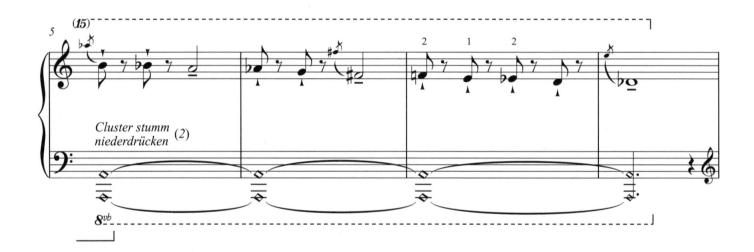

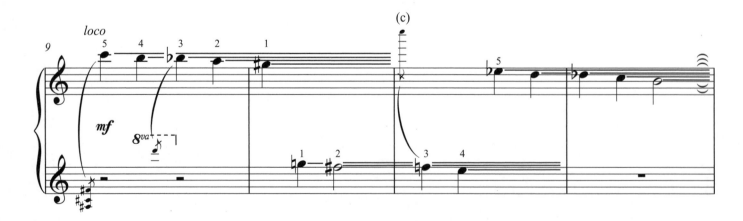

(1) Or one octave on pianos restricted in range.   *(2)* Depress any white note cluster within the octave without sounding.

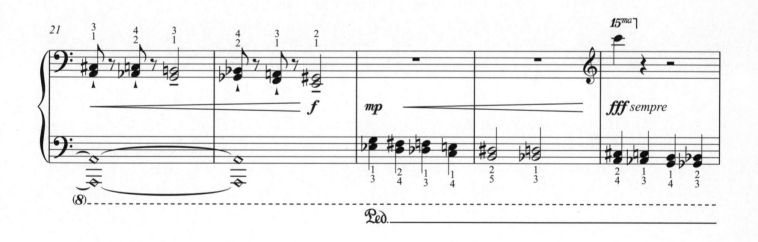

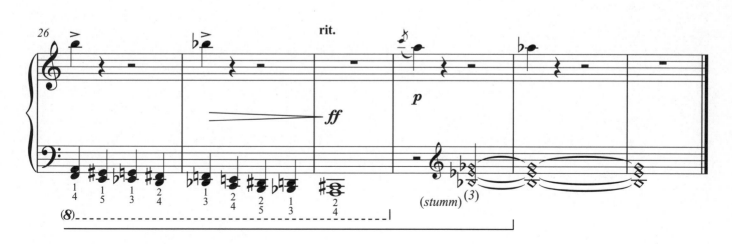

(3) Depress given notes without sounding

[Blank page to facilitate page turns]

Teaching Notes – Grade 5

Allegro con spirito (Kuhlau)

This cheerful movement has moments of grace and charm as well as brilliance and exuberance. Make as much of the dynamic contrasts as possible; they range from *p* to *ff*. The sparkling semiquaver scales and passage work call for clean and precise finger articulation; practise these passages very slowly as you learn the notes and fingering, returning to your slow practice regularly to keep the passage work even and controlled.

Kuhlau marked *legato* and *staccato* where he wanted to specify the touch; unmarked notes can be played at the discretion of the performer. At the start we might lightly detach the RH quavers; hold the dotted crotchet but do not connect it to the quaver that follows (bars 1-2, 5-6, etc). Feel the change of character in the second theme (from bar 13), paying close attention to the articulation markings in the RH.

Am Abend (Hoffmann)

This descriptive piece from the Romantic period is effectively a duo between two singing voices (let's imagine a violin and a cello). You might begin by playing the top RH melody line (stems up) together with the bass line and the pedal, but omitting the accompaniment quavers for a while. Project the lines clearly and shape them beautifully, taking a moment at the end of each phrase to let the music breathe. If you're not sure how to phrase, then sing!

The RH will then need some very careful practice alone. As you balance the main melodic line (stems up) with the accompaniment (stems down), it will help to think of two different dynamic levels (*mp* and *pp*, say). Do this very slowly at first until you have gained the necessary tonal control.

Arietta (Grieg)

Arietta (the first piece from Grieg's 'Lyric Pieces') means 'Little Song', and you might begin by actually playing this beautiful melody alone. Do so expressively, taking time where the music needs it.

Hold on to the long bass E flats (bars 1-4, 15-16), so that when you change the pedal the bass note is still present. Avoid pedalling through the rests, but elsewhere change the pedal as the harmony changes. Where the harmony remains the same but the melody notes change (bars 2, 4, etc), it is best to pedal crotchet beats. In bars 9, 19 etc, aim for finger *legato* in the upper voice if possible.

Cantilena (Camilleri)

This slow and atmospheric *Cantilena* by Maltese composer Charles Camilleri features an ornate melody line over a slow-moving LH in stately crotchets.

Change pedal on each new bass note (mostly first beats), holding the pedal through the whole bar (the idea of pedalling the low basses applies also in bars 18-19, and bars 35-38). Listen carefully so that the texture is well balanced and enjoy the richness and mild dissonance of Camilleri's soundworld. As a general principle, longer RH notes receive more tone that shorter ones. This means minims need to be solid so that they still sound at the end of their duration, and demisemiquavers and grace notes should be played very lightly (as though caressed).

Chinese Carillon (Rozsa)

A study in delicacy and precision of touch, *Chinese Carillon* is a very effective recital piece and an ideal encore. Both hands are written high up in the treble register, imitating the sound of bells. The effect is rather like a mechanical music box – one that winds down at the end.

Put the pedal down before you start, and hold it at least until bar 11 (after which you might want to experiment changing the pedal more often, if you prefer a cleaner sound). From bar 25 the pedal can stay down right until the end. The touch throughout is detached, and because of the presence of the pedal it is not necessary to hold on to all long notes for their full value (ie the minims from bar 7).

Haunted House (Benjamin)

A successful performance of this engaging character piece relies on technical precision and a storytelling in performance. The *sforzando* accents surely refer to things that go bump in the night as we tiptoe cautiously around this haunted house. Exaggerate the accents for dramatic effect, especially the *sff* in bar 4, taking care that the lower level dynamics are well controlled. Suspense builds in bar 26 leading to the chimes of an out-of-tune clock (bars 30-34). As the piece ends, we leave the eerie scene behind us and scamper off into the night.

Staccato quavers need to be dry and very rhythmic, precisely on the beat. Begin each RH scale (ie bar 2) as softly as possible so as to get maximum effect from the swell to the middle of the bar. Bars 11-12 pose a technical challenge, the ability to co-ordinate thumb and upper finger precisely together after the grace notes.

Two-part Invention in Eb (Vaughan Williams)

This two-part invention comes from book 1 of Vaughan Williams' *Six Teaching Pieces for Pianoforte* (1934). Like J S Bach's illustrious models this invention is a duo for the two hands, each of which is equally important. The piece serves as a valuable exercise in developing independence between the hands.

The first statement of the subject spans an octave, from Eb to the next Eb below, although the composer is not too strict about replicating his subject exactly in all subsequent entries (the RH in bar 3 does not quite reach the low tonic, and some later entries are built from fragments of the subject). The main challenge lies in articulation and phrasing, combining different touches between the hands. Thus, one hand may be playing *legato* while the other plays *staccato*; further challenges arise when two-note slurs are added to the mix.

Kettle Rag (Norton)

Ragtime piano originated in America around the turn of the twentieth century, and was made famous by Scott Joplin. Christopher Norton's bright and breezy *Kettle Rag* features LH chords on the weak second beat of the bar, the blue note (the major and minor third of the key in alternation, such as the B and Bb in bars 1-2, the E and Eb in bar 17, etc) and a syncopated feeling throughout.

Play the LH very rhythmically, the *staccato* crotchets dry and punchy. In the RH, carefully observe all *staccato* notes, and shorten the second note in the slurred pairs. Exaggerate all the accents, especially those that come on weak beats.

Allegro con spirito

1st movement from *Sonatina in C*, op. 55 no. 3

Friedrich Kuhlau
(1786-1832)

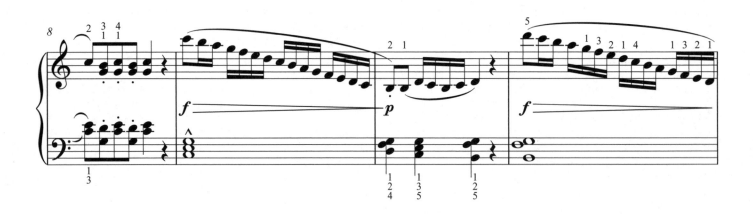

Am Abend

(In the Evening)
op. 88 no. 2

Henrich Hoffmann
(1842-1902)

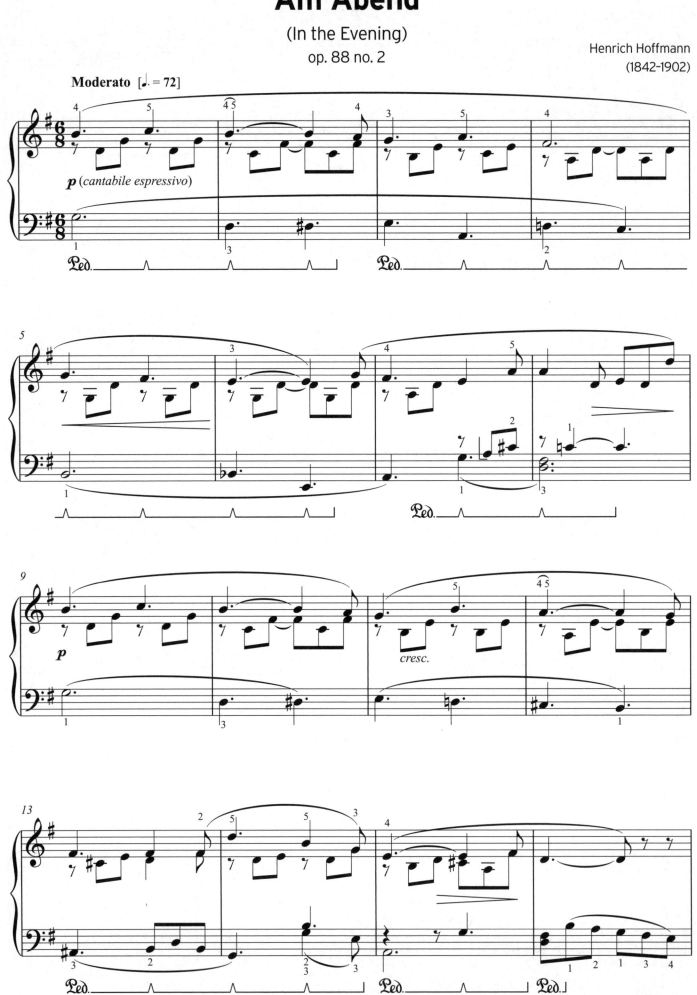

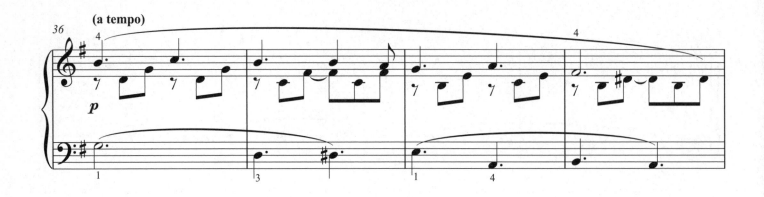

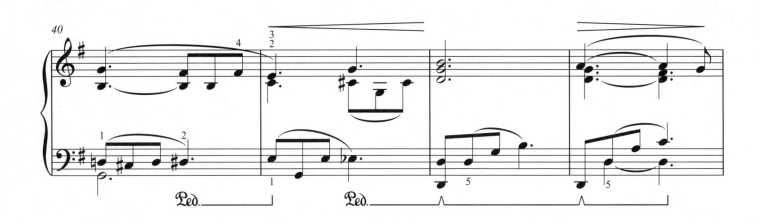

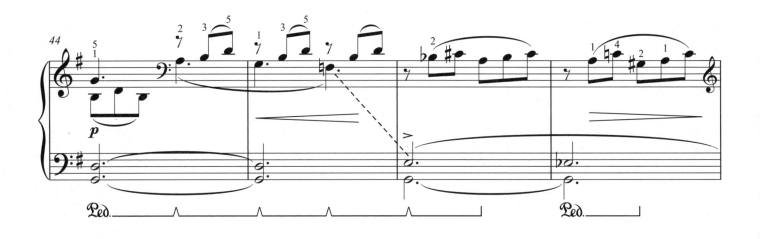

Arietta

op. 12 no. 1

Edvard Grieg
(1843-1907)

Cantilena

Charles Camilleri
(1931-2009)

Chinese Carillon

from *Kaleidoscope*

Miklos Rozsa
(1907-1995)

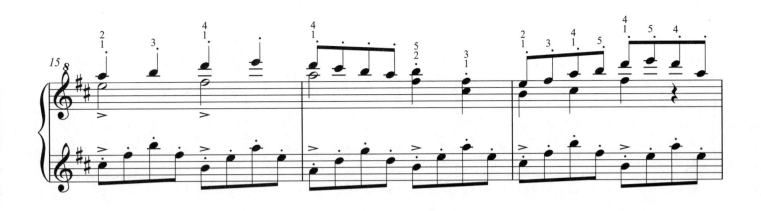

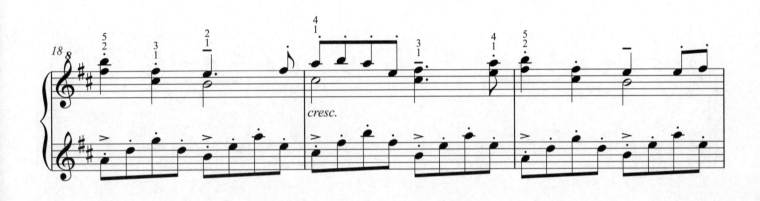

pochissimo rit.

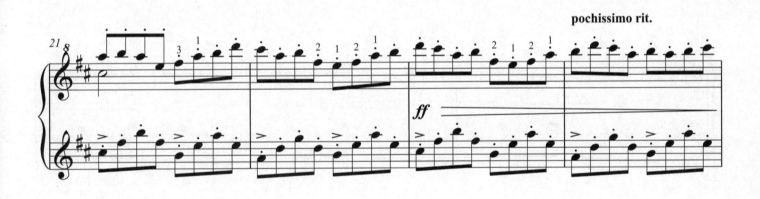

a tempo (come prima)

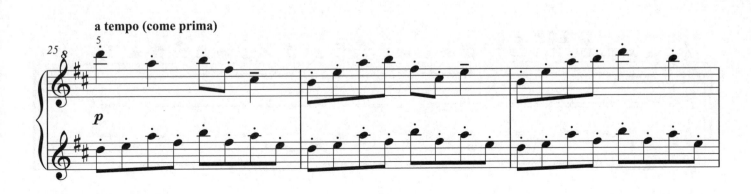

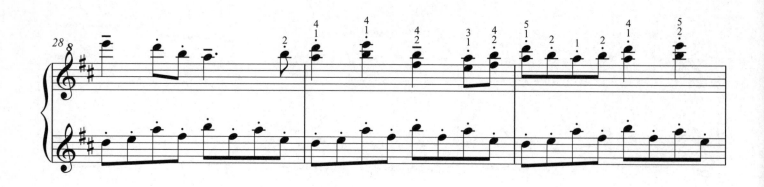

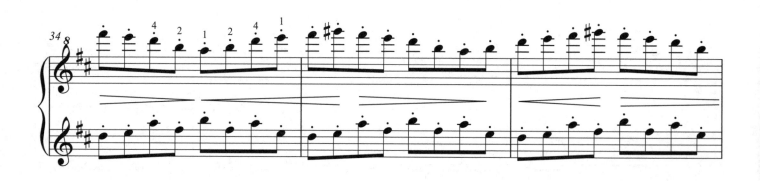

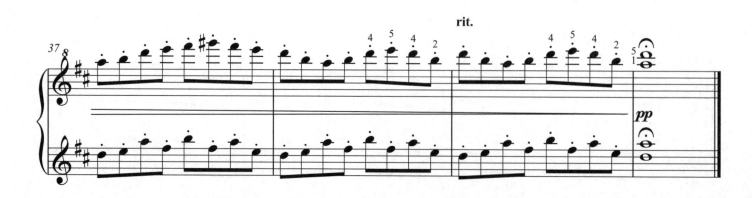

Haunted House

Arthur Benjamin
(1893-1960)

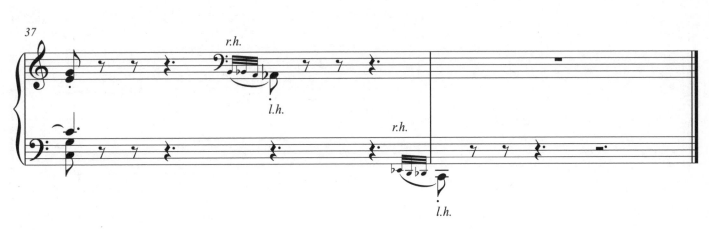

Two-part Invention in E♭

Ralph Vaughan Williams
(1872-1958)

Allegro moderato [♩ = 84]

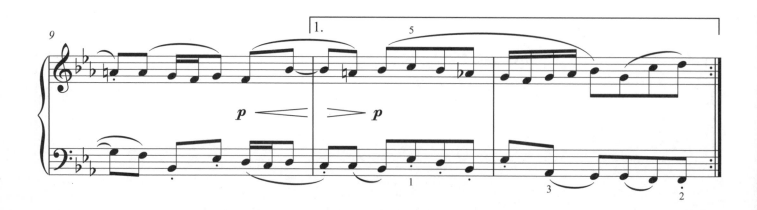

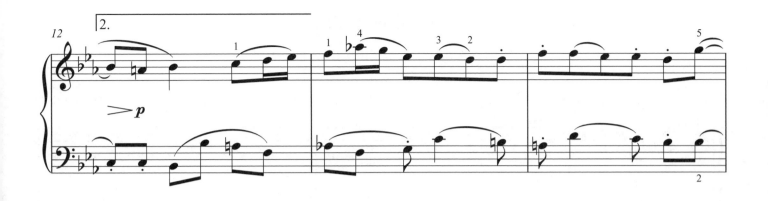

Kettle Rag

from *Lavender's Kind of Blue*

Christopher Norton
(b. 1953)

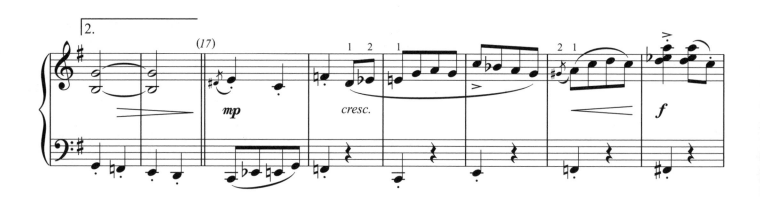

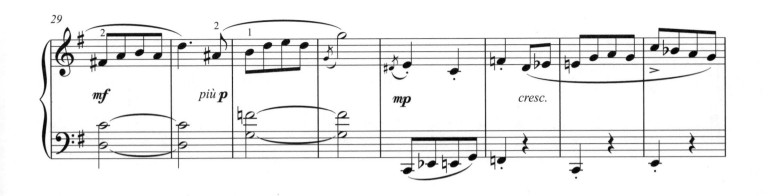

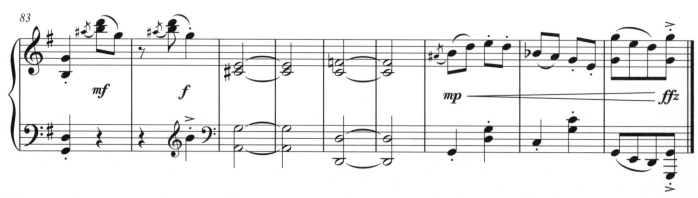